14 . 2 . 87

Happy Valentine's Day!

Love to you both,

Sophie.

JODHPURS
in the
QUANTOCKS

Glen Baxter

JONATHAN CAPE
THIRTY-TWO BEDFORD SQUARE LONDON

also by Glen Baxter

THE FALLS TRACER
THE KHAKI
FRUITS OF THE WORLD IN DANGER
THE HANDY GUIDE TO AMAZING PEOPLE
CRANIREONS OV BOTYA
STORIES
THE WORKS
THE IMPENDING GLEAM
ATLAS
HIS LIFE: THE YEARS OF STRUGGLE

"Callens" and "The Merest Dwindle" first appeared
in *5×5*, ed. Asa Benveniste (Trigram Press, 1981).
Some of the drawings have previously appeared in the
Observer, the *Mail on Sunday* and *Vanity Fair* (USA).
Many of them are in private collections in Great
Britain and the United States. Glen Baxter exhibits his
work at the Nigel Greenwood Gallery in London and
at the Holly Solomon Gallery in New York.

First published 1986
Copyright © 1986 by Glen Baxter
Jonathan Cape Ltd, 32 Bedford Square, London WC1B 3EL

British Library Cataloguing in Publication Data

Baxter, Glen
Jodhpurs in the Quantocks.
1. English wit and humour, Pictorial
I. Title
741.5'942   NC1479

ISBN 0-224-02872-3

Printed in Great Britain
by St Edmundsbury Press, Bury St Edmunds, Suffolk

For Clark Coolidge

Another Tuesday

PELLETS CONTINUED to thud into the baize uprights. I awoke amidst a clamour of voice and cymbal. I poured out a glass. My room had only recently been vacated by a contingent from Essex and I felt I needed time to erase all signs of their tumult.

"Any noodle will make a fire," roared Edna.

I suspect that I was meant to make some remark, but I chose instead to ignore this fierce brute with the ungainly shoulders. She pulled off her steaming macintosh. The bald thought gripped me then – she might stay. The significance of every detail seemed to amuse her.

"Quite appalling. I don't think much of that," she spluttered, kicking the cupboard in a smooth, burnished loop.

"It does have its own radiator," I noted.

"To be a piece of machinery is not enough," came the reply.

A greasy rope rattled down.

"I'll be nipping along," Edna remarked, placing her forehead against the twine.

It was with mingled misunderstanding and regret that I watched her go. I actually thought of the room again as a mere platform of wattle and brick. Crude habits of thought and design came to me, washed over an image of her immobile, striking face. I could hear her voice once more, "Aye aye! Pump away!" Alone now, with these countless trivialities, I entered the wardrobe.

It was some fifteen minutes later that I heard the bell. The wooden gears had held up and not seized. I felt both surprised and pleased. A return to normalcy seemed a distinct possibility.

The next morning Godfrey took his feet off the sofa and sat up. We of the Brotherhood pretended not to notice, and busied ourselves in the quilts. A shaft of light pierced the gloom of the refectory.

"What shall we do for breakfast?" asked Kenneth, as he brushed the soot from his arm. We had been informed that the mailcoach from London was due to stop at Brightling at 7.00 and so we took the opportunity of opening up the pilchards. Mr Featherstone had troubled to remove his hat, so the operation was conducted with the minimum of fuss. At 7.15 all was in readiness. Godfrey had positioned himself behind the dovecote, and Edna was busy hacking at the topiary hedge by the gate. I took my place on the kitchen table next to the sleeping figure of Mr Featherstone, and peered through the kitchen window down the gravel drive.

When the coach arrived, Godfrey was first on the scene. He took the small brown parcel and disappeared round the back of the house. Mr Featherstone woke up, reached for his hat and set out after him. Edna dropped her shears and joined in the chase. There seemed little else to do but adjust the clock in the lobby and return the hinges to the study door. How wrong I was. At the stroke of 10.00, Edna, bloodied yet unbowed, burst through the door.

"I'm through with this tramping," she announced.

There was something about her demeanour that indicated a change of outlook. I bent down to pick up the hinges once more.

"Look here," snapped Edna, somewhat sharply. She was holding out her arm. It smelled faintly of camphor.

"I'm afraid I know nothing about that," I replied, sensing trouble.

"Give me two dollars," demanded Edna. Her eyes seemed larger now.

I dug both hands into my pockets and pretended to search for the money. After twenty minutes of my rustling and delving, I sensed that Edna was getting restless. My life was clearly in danger. The next thing I noticed was the sunlight reflected on the shaft of the steel spanner that was arcing toward my temple.

When I awoke, Edna was gone, the Brotherhood colours had been ripped from the walls and Mr Featherstone was standing upright by the remains of the study door. Several powerful steel fans kept him up although he was swaying quite markedly. He spoke softly of Edna's leaving and the rumpus at the General Meeting. He pointed to the hinges scattered across the floor. I could see the tears welling up in his eyes. It was almost too much. I had no choice but to reach out and take up the spanner.

As the train pulled out of Smotling station I turned my head for one last look at the old house that had come to mean so much to me. Mr Featherstone had taken up his position by the gate and Edna had returned with a stocky shopkeeper from the north.

IT WAS AT CHAUNDLEY CAMP THAT I
FIRST LEARNED TO SET FIRE TO MY OWN
KNEECAPS

WITH GRIM DETERMINATION THE TWO
CLUNG DESPERATELY TO THE FOSSILS

"SO JUST EXACTLY WHAT IS THIS REVOLUTIONARY BREAKTHROUGH IN FURNITURE DESIGN OF YOURS,EH?" SNAPPED THE IMPATIENT LUCINDA

The March

MR THOMPSON FLICKED his lapels up with unerring ease. Shivering passengers at the little Russian station looked on with studied indifference. They knew they had left their Sussex homes in bright sunshine for this. Mr Thompson brushed his lapels down again. He knew that painstaking and accurate mistakes were being made, but he also realized it was precisely that which made not the slightest difference. He seemed to understand the darkness.

"Getting restive?" inquired the line of passengers.

"I like to see more fog . . . usually," answered Mr Thompson. He had sold Hoovers across most of Europe and he felt he knew how to respond to such direct questioning.

One of the passengers, a stockily built man of about forty-five, stepped forward and beamed at Mr Thompson.

"I suppose you want my homburg," sighed Mr Thompson, "I should have guessed."

There was little time to lose now. One hand on his lapel and the other moving up towards the homburg, Mr T. turned and fled down the platform. It was August Bank Holiday, and fumes were coming from all the major tunnels. There were three notice-boards announcing this. Ignoring all three, Mr T. ducked under the ticket barrier, darted past an astounded official and round the corner into the yard. It seemed even darker now. Whistles were blowing in the night. A horse and carriage galloped by. There was a distinct rumble and a flash. Mr T. scrambled up a narrow incline and out on to a large, flat granite slab. An untidy mound of greasy tarpaulins over by the stockyard wall seemed to offer temporary shelter. He hurried over. Lifting a corner of the heavy green cloth, he slid underneath. His mind was racing now. Should he call Halifax? Outside the night seemed filled with running footsteps, whistles and occasional gunshots.

When he awoke, crowds of gaping, white-faced onlookers were gathered round, in a state of unusual irritability. He spoke to them perfunctorily about the benefits of spring water. He was taken downtown to a shabby wooden building, where he was introduced to the Rector and his wife. They nodded politely, for they believed in being seen to be grim. Listening to the nine o'clock news helped.

"Water has many medicinal properties . . . " announced Mr Thompson.

"That may well be," retorted the Rector's wife, "but I believe in the largest possible gin."

Thompson realized that the only course of action left open to him was to feign sleep.

The next day being Sunday, dinner was at nine. The only comfortable chair in the kitchen was occupied by a surly Methodist. He was contemplating a large tin of ham. "Vinegar," he was mumbling. "Bring vinegar." It was clear he could not face Mrs Verretrom's shredded cabbage.

The following Sunday was even more airless and sultry. "A Message to Beet Growers" was on the radio. Thompson found himself smiling inwardly. Should he reach out for the radio or take one last noggin? He set off to look for the decanter and crashed into the wardrobe. The red light went out at once.

"I am a broadcaster," he shouted, and stumbled forward into the piles of *Reader's Digests* on the sofa. He adjusted his trousers for the fourth time that day and blundered off into the hallway. Outside, the snow was falling again.

Strange Customs
of Many Lands

Vowel Study, St Agnes Eve
Brocklehampton

"DURING MY YEARS OUT EAST I MANAGED
TO PICK UP ONE OR TWO TIPS ON THE
ART OF RELAXATION" EXPLAINED HOLDSWORTH

AS THE EVENING DEEPENED INTO TWILIGHT
AND HE FELT HIMSELF BECOME RESTLESS AND
FEVERISH, SCRUNDLEY TURNED ONCE AGAIN
TO THE HORN...

Return to Huntleigh

WHEN CAROLINE AWOKE, the pale sun of a winter afternoon filled the entire courtyard and pulled up sharply at the steps. She looked out. "I'll allow that," she muttered, "but I'll need an explanation." The thought of a Mercedes coupé and twelve servants helps enormously. She jumped up feeling somewhat better already. Her personal future with Enid had seemed marginally bleak. She had once done what one has to do as she had known instinctively she ought. Now she was not so sure. Both women had, however, gained much from the friendship. They were rebellious, discontented and longing for excitement, but that was before the reunion. Now they seemed adamantly determined to suffer apart.

It was the morning after their return to Huntleigh.

The logs shifted and dropped in the hearth. Caroline spent the morning in the library, preparing it for the leather merchant. He would soon be here she reckoned. His knock was something she expected to hear, but she would not have the least compunction about sending him away. She hid herself behind a stack of green ledgers. It was just two hours before midnight when the leather merchant appeared. He was already grumbling about the price of a bed. Taking a double handful of coins, he put them in a drawer in the hall. Gradually the colour returned to his pallid countenance. He seemed to have the glimmerings of a plan in his head. He knew there were already several dealers in Spanish leather in the vicinity, but he dealt only in leathers from Córdoba and there were others he was considering. For the first time in his life he was grateful for silken hose, for it certainly did not scratch. He slipped off his pouch and laid it on the table. The night passed uneasily. The great clock in the gallery struck the hour of three twice. The merchant awoke to find the determined figure of Caroline standing squarely above him.

"You are a courageous lad," she muttered.

"Now that I recall, madam, I am indeed," spluttered the hapless merchant. Caroline felt her wan cheeks stiffening with resolve at this.

"Welcome to Huntleigh," she announced, spitting out each word.

Her thoughts were drifting in disconnected fragments now. She crossed swiftly to the window, her anger seemingly dissipated. A knock sounded on the door of the outer chamber. Caroline surveyed herself in the glass. A severe line heightened her pleasure as she leaned forward. It was, without doubt, almost enthralling. But there were other things to consider.

The thunderous knocking continued on the great oak door. Tristram's arm was surely swelling by the minute. His head was probably rolling from side to side. Caroline drew back the latch. Tristram, now semi-conscious, tottered in, clutching his sconce. The leather merchant looked up. Already new designs for pouches were flooding through his mind. He chuckled softly, but the effort was too much for him, and he soon joined Tristram on the floor. Caroline looked down at them both with a wry smile. An unpleasant numbness was creeping into her limbs although she was breathing well within her capacity. Nothing seemed to matter any more. She was only aware of a kind of scraping.

"Breakfast," she croaked. Her voice barely pierced the density of the air beyond her teeth. It was, however, useless. She knew only too well that Enid, the young madcap, was already at work chiselling out the kitchen drawers.

JANET SET ASIDE AN HOUR EACH DAY
TO WORK ON HER THREATENING LETTERS

MANY FRUITFUL HOURS WERE SPENT
SCRUTINIZING COLONEL FOTHERINGTON'S TWEEDS

FELICITY HAD RESERVED A SOMEWHAT
LESS THAN LUKEWARM RECEPTION FOR
HER SOCIAL WORKER

The Binelace File

THROUGH THE DUSK, gleaming dully, the rippling thighs of the Commandant beckoned. Saul scowled and grunted. "The Little Englishman" the Egyptians called him, for he wore a patched shirt and a belt of silk despite his advancing years. The dervishes often rolled over in dozens when he took the air. They were right. He began the day with every muscle relaxed, walking with ease through the busy market squares.

"It has become necessary to utilize all our pockets," he roared, ignoring the knotty sticks carried by the furious dervishes. Mr Zachary searched him keenly with his grey eyes but could find little expression of dismay and fear. There was no sign of earth in the central room either. Saul often raked under the bluish-grey canopy and afterwards relaxed with a charcoal stump. He could, on reflection, easily upset the most virtuous intentions. Although he lived only five miles from Boscombe, he remained an object of shame and reproach. Mr Zachary realized this and turned his gaze boldly, yet respectfully, up and away. He came presently to the little form that Saul had been working on since March. He looked down. Saul had taken a thin strip of common deal and marked it A–B. Then, with a small brass head soldered on one side, he had laid in another strut, one inch deep, connected to A–B at F. Around this he had excavated a circle with a circumference that seemed curiously adequate. Mr Zachary stood back, scraped the earth from his boots and eyed the somewhat sodden mass for some time. His figure had stiffened noticeably, but he heeded it not.

Pendrell was looming dimly in the doorway now, one hand toying with his trouser pocket. He was holding a small piece of bread. Timidly, he drew it forth. Mr Zachary seemed momentarily to lose control, and with a little cry of anguish lurched forward. He had to force himself to remember the meaning of stability. A scuffle ensued.

Soon the bullet got the better of the knotty stick and Mr Zachary lay on the oak floor of the station house. Pendrell spoke of him later that evening from the relative quiet of the Main Tub Room.

"Mr Zachary is a man who sleeps," he announced. He was trying to think clearly now, but Saul remained unconvinced. He was seated by the window, reading aloud from *At Worcester with Chessington*. A sense of purpose filled him completely. He began to lurch. His jacket, the right sleeve of which had only recently been altered, reached fully to his waist. With a tug he pulled it back up by the shoulder, turned it into a double fold and was gone, along the narrow walkway and up on to the platform overlooking Luxor. He remained there for a brief spell, adjusting his folds and gazing out into the purple night. A crowd of Egyptians gathered round, whistling and jeering. He had no alternative but to return to his room. He placed both hands on the rope ladder and began to go slowly up, intent on ignoring the clamour from below. His head entered a thin layer of steam. He pulled up his legs. Seating himself on the edge of his bunk he began his nocturnal task, the task he had for so long postponed. He was home again now, tasting the ashes, and scraping the mould from the Binelace File.

"I APPEAR TO HAVE LEFT YOUR SANDWICHES
BACK ON ALPHA IV, OLD MAN" HISSED BLAKE

IT WAS JUST AS I FEARED. DESPITE MY PROTESTS,
HE WAS ABOUT TO RUN THROUGH HIS THREE-HOUR
PROGRAMME ONCE AGAIN

ON DAMP AUTUMN EVENINGS, BJORN WOULD
SEEK THE SOLACE OF HIS GRAPHITE COLLECTION

Sunset over Dudley

THE PORTUGUESE LOOMED up from behind an overturned stroganoff. His legs seemed unsteady. His name was Vrom. "All right, Angela," he was saying. Her fork dropped into the broccoli. She had only a split second to make her move.

"I've got a hunch you're in some kind of trouble . . ." she began.

He waved a tiny jewelled axe at her.

"And you've been talking to that Sinclair Duggan again, haven't you," she added, rolling her tongue round the double g in Duggan.

"Uh uh," he replied.

"Not romantic, but typical," she noted. There was thought mirrored now in her flashing eyes.

"You can get back to your meal now," she hissed.

He tore off in the direction of the kitchen. His eyes were dark and his mouth clamped to a thin grey line. It seemed as if in one flash his thought had crystallized into adamant resolve. This time he knew it, though.

"What is romance without finance?" he asked, pounding his clenched fists into his tweed blouson. It was some time before his cogitations ceased.

In the bustle of those first few hours at the surgery, Angela had sensed the beginnings of a thrill. Her colleagues had noticed it too, and there had been one or two ugly scenes before the lighting track was replaced. The flushed, sheepish faces had not deterred her, for alone she knew the agony of long, wet afternoons listening to other people's complaints.

The door swung open. The Portuguese was back.

"Nut?" he inquired.

It seemed an odd feast, but yet she complied.

"I was delayed until I came," he added, sitting down next to her.

The brooding senior jerked to life. Angela realized he had become a public danger, and now, with the Portuguese by her side also, she felt decidedly uneasy. The Portuguese leaned over.

"Fond of pets?" he queried. "I can arrange things."

For upwards of a minute a strange feeling of disinterest flooded the room. Then Angela spoke.

Kirk, despite his impediment, had managed to reach the sofa. He had left Tucson only that morning. Now he was urging another visit to the roof. The clanging of bells was what he longed for most. Angela knew this and shied a slipper in his direction.

Kirk caught it in his teeth.

"It's all I crave," he beamed, "and more than I could expect."

"Then here you go," Angela growled, and tossed over another.

Kirk expressed his approval with a somewhat more dulcet grunt than was usual. His nostrils dilated with pleasure and he began to slump.

The unwanted clamour and sign of delight had evidently unnerved the Portuguese. He was taking deep breaths and counting with his fingers. Angela recognized the symptoms.

"Dr Judd will see you now," she said, pointing to the door.

"You scug," he exploded, "I'm off."

That was the last that Angela ever saw of him. She peeled off her coat and began to retrace her steps until she came up to the dangling rope. She stopped here to admire the view. A chill wind was whistling across a gigantic expanse of mud beyond which lay a man-made gully decorated with red and white bunting. It had been a long time since Angela had dusted there, and the slogan SEX FOR NEW BOYS was only a distant memory now.

Strange Customs
of Many Lands

Turnip Worship,
Antwerp

IT WAS YOUNG ALF'S FIRST ENCOUNTER WITH
SOPHISTICATED NIGHT LIFE IN THE BIG CITY

New Ways
With
Vegetables
1

Aubergines

Connecticut

THE APARTMENT was messy though a Calder mobile hung overhead. Once or twice Larry had talked. "Sure," he said. That way he could devote his time to studying chemistry. He was five feet tall.

On Wednesday, when he had two dollars and a bus ticket home, he decided to take two pictures. He photographed two elongated mounds with some difficulty. He was a little nervous and hoped they wouldn't fit into the picture. Then he stood up and took a list of things in the apartment, camera above his head, pointing down, so that he was able to include his right hand in the shots.

That night he went out to meet Natalie at the gym. She told him that she remembered a Perry Mason sculpture in the Connecticut museum. He aimed the camera down at her feet and said nothing.

Late Friday afternoon she decided that what she really needed was to have him like her. She took a master's degree in chemistry, bought an Instamatic camera, and gave him a haircut. She really did study for the chemistry exam, taking the train to a larger, more impressive university. She saw students wandering through the art museum which was not far away. There was only one piece of sculpture there – flaky yellow and black plastic foam stuck to a tiny wheel. It had nothing to say. Natalie snapped a picture, wondering what made her do it. This was an automatic reaction with her.

At night she and Larry ate spaghetti and drank beer from heavy glass mugs. She doubted if Larry ever went to see Mose Allison.

"I make spaghetti," he replied. He could raise his neck with no trouble though, so his troubles didn't amount to much. As they were finishing dinner he asked Natalie to move some of the furniture around. She turned on the radio. Larry talked in time with the music. They each smoked one mentholated cigarette and then went up the way an umbrella opens. Larry's face changed. Natalie looked round at him, at the front edge of his thumb resting on the table. One end of his thick maroon scarf depressed her. She felt awkward, but could not let it go on. She ran her hands down and round in circles wide enough to make Larry nod. He stood on tiptoe to reach her, standing and staring. She stepped back and took a pearl decoration from the music rack.

"That's it," she said. She looked at him. She was fast losing her senses. Food was beginning to smell like a 1976 Volvo.

Sometimes Larry would take her hand and pull himself up. Natalie found herself putting both her arms behind her back. She felt Larry's scarf bunched up against the cushion next to her. Natalie looked down in surprise.

"My God," she cried. "Are you five feet tall?"

The next day she went back to the museum to point out the sculpture. She paused behind the rope. She didn't look at it. She couldn't. She was already thinking about the spaghetti.

WRONGDOERS WERE SENT UP TO MR WILKS
FOR EXTRA WORK ON THE PUMICE

VERONICA HAD HIT UPON A SCHEME FOR
DEALING WITH BOLSOVER'S PACKED DEFENCE

THERE WAS BARELY ENOUGH TIME FOR ME TO
CAST A CRITICAL EYE OVER THE SEAMWORK
ON HIS LEGGINGS...

Trampling at Ongar

BROMWARD SMILED. He made his way to the library. There, on the big folding table he kept the blades in Vaseline. He had decided to think of something, but he was wrong, so he halted there and then. The hall was in total darkness. Three vertical pillars of soot hung from the ceiling. He paused before opening the door to the library. He stepped inside. The librarian sneezed in a theatrical way, leaning slightly forward.

"*Heraldic Devices*, Volume Two," snapped Bromward.

"Coom – er – ell – ter – nat," replied the librarian, pointing with his left hand towards the far end of the room. There was an awkward silence before Bromward shuffled off.

He approached the dark, mahogany shelves. He scanned the circle of grey-green books lined up there. Three titles caught his attention. *The Art of Destruction, What are Tablemats For?* and *Promoting Waistcoats.* His face lit up as he caught sight of an embossed urn on the spine of a large, leather-bound volume. He took down the copy of *Introducing the Blimp* and carried it to the main desk.

Later that afternoon, he was lurching through the fog, clutching his prize. He looked out the window of the bus at the drifting leaves. By sheer fistwork he had reached this position, and he was not about to relinquish it lightly. He recalled his first visit to the library when he had taken the precaution of wearing an extra cardigan. *Sex for New Boys* was one of the first titles he had taken out then. Since that time he had moved on to *Displaying Footwear, Using the Elbow* and *Forgo that Ceremony.* He could get on with the committee. They certainly understood the darkness. Only once had they admonished him. He had elected to fill his own fountain-pen when it obviously didn't work. That evening, every seat on the bus seemed to be occupied by loud-voiced overpainted sailors and the like. It was clearly not an ideal situation. He had brooded over this for weeks afterwards.

Even now he could not bear the thought of unpainted naval personnel.

Today, however, was different. He was determined to remain awake. He raised a laugh, a protest, then another laugh. He was soon home. A tiny, bald Austrian opened the door, his thin hand flying quickly round to the edge of the brass latch.

"Enjoy it?" inquired Bromward.

Pemberthy began to splutter.

"It's ... my ... thumb," he cried. His high, piping voice sounded like an old recording. Bromward remained unmoved, though. He knew that it was coming. When the red light went out, he stepped smartly forward. There was a large rectangular polished lever straight in front of him. One touch would ensure a copy of the *Listener* and *Horace Calling,* but he did not have time now. His legs, encased in their trousers, quickened their pace. There seemed to be an odd assortment of coats and Norfolk jackets in the hall. It would require a lengthy explanation from Pemberthy, reasoned Bromward, and he was not sure he could take it. Instead he staggered into the lounge. Wendover was there to greet him and remove his glasses.

"I've had a letter ..." stammered Wendover.

"About thirty vellum-bound editions?" queried Bromward, somewhat nervously.

"I've read a great deal, but never have I countenanced such a thing," said Wendover.

"That sounds distressing," added Bromward.

"Chronic is more precise," rasped back Wendover.

It was then that Bromward noticed that Wendover was wearing a magenta shirt with a mud-coloured tie. The light was dazzling. Bromward tugged his sleeve.

"Ever hear my voice?" he asked Wendover in a hoarse whisper.

"Er ... yes," came the reply.

"Well, I like to put up my feet as much as possible," said Bromward.

"I understand. You don't look anaemic. I'll get the Spam. You rest," blurted Wendover, suddenly aware of his position. Bromward settled down into a comfortable chair and began leafing through *The Controller Speaks.* He knew it to be a fairly lightweight tome, not in the same league as *Last Load Arriving,* but he needed to relax, and soon there would be the welcome distraction of dinner.

Two hours later, the gong sounded. Sir Charles Wrexham had decided to join them. He was a somewhat careless diner, and it was usually Bromward's trousers that suffered. Sir Charles tilted his glass.

"Troost up thee to one another," he beamed. The other two downed their

Beaujolais in silence, preferring not to encourage the old duffer. His eyes flashed with fury, but he knew he must bide his time and wait for the proper moment.

"Were you ever in the bicycle sheds?" observed Wendover, raising a forkful of veal to his lips.

"My sweet," remonstrated Sir Charles, "about once a week, on average."

"Mustn't jigger up the kidneys, you know," he added somewhat later.

Bromward's knife clattered to his plate.

"You know," began Sir Charles, "I usually go in for fits of hysteria, always on the dot of seven, with a tray of porridge . . ." his voice trailed off.

"We take a glass dish of tinned salmon, followed by a Bakewell pudding," noted Wendover.

"Well, that's as maybe," remarked Bromward, "but Sir Charles can have little idea of the nature of our calling."

"I know it sounds invidious," said Sir Charles, "but I am here."

His voice came to a dulcet falsetto as he got out of his seat and began to help himself to whisky.

Wendover glanced at Bromward. Together they set their faces toward the decanter with a bitter smile. For one unforgiving minute they leaned forward in their chairs before deciding that only a complete failure to keep abreast of current affairs had led them to this. They both realized that it was late and probably a Sunday, but that was about all. Wendover sucked noisily on a hollow tooth and shifted his feet beneath the blue rug.

Strange Customs
of Many Lands

Pumice Blessing,
Auckland,   N.Z.
May 3rd & 6th

SOON AFTER MY ARRIVAL IN OSLO, MRS UNSWORTH
SHOWED ME TO MY QUARTERS

SERGEANT RAWLINGS HAD ALMOST FOUND
A WAY OF COPING WITH THE BOREDOM OF
THE LONG EASTER WEEKEND

The System

LIKE THE HUB of a wheel, Fairbanks lies near the centre of a vast trade area encompassing hundreds of square miles of Alaska's rugged interior. Weeks' Fields on the edge of the city is constantly bordered by rows of busy looters. Dozens of airplanes are stripped daily. In the ruins of a deserted Alaskan Airlines office I met Noel Threadgate, one of the handful of oldtime looters who pioneered Alaskan aviation looting in the early 1920s. As late as 1941 he and his family of eight were stripping every known make of plane of radios, wheels, mirrors, seats and aviation equipment.

"Our Fairbanks landing field was a ball park in the old days," Threadgate recalled. "I took everything from an old Dakota, but still had to smack the ground and grind to a zigzag stop with my head."

Today multi-engined planes, well equipped with security devices are almost completely dismantled overnight. The stolen parts are sold as far away as Anchorage to the south and Nome to the west. Dozens of isolated trading centres and villages in the interior depend on the illicit trading of these plane parts for their supplies. At a small mining camp named Chicken Fifteen, gold miners and many of their families worship Johnny Lynn. He is essential for their continued existence. Often he brings them whole cockpits, and one especially harsh winter a complete B-36. As Johnny, a young ex-GI from Boston explained, "We've got roads now. From them we can get into thousands of airfields the oldtimers couldn't even touch. We can take more equipment and stay longer. Forty years ago we were a gold-rush town. Today we're an air-base boom town. I don't think we'll ever be a normal city."

THERE WERE, OF COURSE, THE ENDLESSLY
BORING LUNCHES

"ALLOW ME TO EXPLAIN THE REASON FOR
MY SLIGHT DELAY IN GETTING HERE..."
BEGAN THE PADRE

GREAT FAILURES
OF OUR TIME

N⁰ 32

The First Billiard Cue

The Exact Place

MRS SCRANTON and her daughter are trying to view the garden more clearly. A cloth bluebird stands in the earth. The doctor comes by.

The sky is overcast and the lake is calm. Much is growing imprecise now. The ancestral land is under water, purplish in the late October haze. No details, only the low picket fence of the island where Bosgrove lives. A plain, broad-faced girl, no more than seventeen, watches the water collect and drip the hundred yards or so down a kind of funnel into an iron trench.

Leaves are falling, and the funnel, closed for the winter, is now almost pure white. Creamy-coloured blocks impede further progress and so she stops. She begins to take it in.

"It has to be the way it looks," she says to herself, not once or twice, but three and four times.

Mrs Scranton and her daughter observe all this from their window. They know it is a little troublesome, but choose not to discuss it. The doctor can speak loudly enough, though. He has the Croix de Guerre. He also knows it is unethical to feel any pain. It is purely a matter of principle. Mrs Scranton leans and raises her daughter to a near sitting position beneath her quilted dress.

"I haven't been able to do that for months," she says. "Thank you, doctor."

"That will be two hundred and seventy five pounds," he announces.

"Thank you again," she says. "The deal is complete."

The doctor counts out the notes. There is enough for dinner in the city all right. He knows that. Mrs Scranton doesn't like to be touched, though. He knows that too. She wears dinner gloves. She is trying hard not to be "ordinary" any more.

The clock chimes. It is very near six o'clock. The sky is still overcast. The bluebird has gone and a long diagonal crack has appeared in the funnel.

THE SUMMER TERM WAS ALWAYS
A BITTER DISAPPOINTMENT

New Ways
With
Vegetables
2

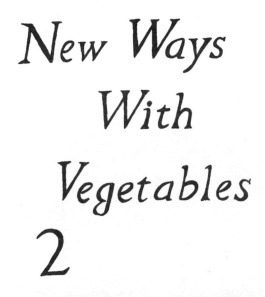

Parsnips

SLOWLY, BUT WITH UNERRING PRECISION
DR TUTTLE REACHED FOR HIS LUGER...

Thelft

Alma had made her way up to the bench. Work on the magneto followed. She took a plug spanner and wrapped this in brown paper. Next, she brought out a roll of tape which she drew over the webbing of her chair. Holding a spanner flat against the upholstery, she was able to put her left hand on the floor. A single, shaded light burned in the centre of the bench. Outside, a dark building showed, and the mob in the driveway remained sullenly motionless. This was perfect timing. Breathing fast, listening intently, Alma lifted the pliers up by her shoulder. She had learnt what she wanted to know. There would be no need of wax and binding now. Mr Lemax was still in evidence in one corner of the room alongside his bureau – a huge, cumbersome thing. Alma knew it had to be a fake. She had only managed to ease out of it a tiny roll of paper. Her fingers had closed tightly over it as Mr Lemax had discussed her future at the tea-rooms. But that was all over now. His whispered remarks were almost soundless. He sat by the window, examining it carefully. Stefan Zeig Dacher waited his turn outside, drumming on the glass.

Almost as though he understood, Mr Lemax went quickly out of the room. In a minute he was back again. Two or three minutes later the manager appeared with an ugly bruise on his cheek. Alma spoke abruptly to him, laid down her pliers and started up the engine. Mr Lemax came over. As he spoke he slipped his fingers inside his overalls and brought out a wad of paper. He had dusted it barely two hours before. Now he dropped it squarely on to the bench. Alma reacted violently, pummelling the wood with her fists. It was never meant to be like this, she reasoned. The old man was supposed to show.

She whirled round, and as her whirling thoughts broke, she became aware of a tall, greying figure at her side nodding with a kind of inward elation. It was Stefan Zeig Dacher. Alma fingered her collar thoughtfully, then stood up. Out in the corridor were Brill and Hartley. She was safe enough. Yet the figure at her side seemed somehow dangerous in his lurching. Maybe it was the light from the magneto on his lip. It didn't seem to matter now, though. The mob outside would soon be switching on the Electric Grin. Alma realized it was all over for her. Her future at the tea-rooms seemed assured and Mr Lemax would not be leaving in a hurry. She closed her eyes and picked up the pliers.

MANY WERE THE OCCASIONS WHEN I CHOSE
NOT TO PARTICIPATE IN THOSE EARNEST
AFTER-DINNER DEBATES

EDNA WAS HAVING PROBLEMS WITH HER
HOLIDAY ACCOMMODATION

WE ELECTED NOT TO DISTURB HIM WHILST HE
WAS ENGAGED IN SUCH COMPLEX CALCULATIONS

Adjusting the Mower

WINDS OF UP TO fifteen miles an hour gusted up and down the tiny town. M. Vautier was standing very still, erect, almost at attention.

"Mais, c'est pour Confort Moderne," he announced. That proved to be accurate. Intermittently, that night, the boulevard lights flashed off and on. About five in the morning, the residents of the eastern end of the street came wading in. They knew they were awake – at last – after two decades of dillydallying. M. Vautier was in control again. He moved his eyebrows up and down independently of one another. A group of Cabinet Ministers sidled past. They would never forget how he looked at that moment. Next to arrive was Alice, the coalman's wife. Then the farriers, the florists, and old Dr Champoule. There were others, but M. Vautier chose to ignore them. He had ideas about becoming a broker.

"Can I help you?" inquired Dr Champoule.

"No, thank you. The supervisor will do just that," replied Vautier.

The doctor glanced at him disapprovingly and smiled. M. Vautier raised his left eyebrow. It was entertaining, derivative, and slight. Not as much could be said for any French museum. M. Vautier's head inclined itself a little more towards the setting sun. He had had his fill of museums anyhow, and right now the only thing that interested him was the dynamics of marketing an array of practically indestructible buttons. Traffic continued to funnel down the darkened streets, with headlights picking out various features of architectural interest.

There was something uncanny about the gaiety that evening in Ghent. Some of the inhabitants took it calmly, others ranted and raved. Sandwiches were burnt openly in the streets. Crowds swelled up and down the sides of the main square. Tubular chairs were hoisted aloft and many leading figures were hooted and obstructed.

His head bowed low, M. Vautier made his way past the hundreds of exasperated people. A Turk turned to him. "Sit down," he said, and was gone. The sound of a jazz band drifted out from a distant café.

M. Vautier considered making his way there, but decided he could not get involved after all. He was spending fifty to sixty pounds a year on brackets and he had to be careful. He remembered the Grammarian's promise and the ensuing burglary at the Town Hall. It all seemed so clear now. A cardboard box, flattened almost into a floppy wedge of brown and grey floated by, borne aloft on the evening wind. It seemed as if it were the size of a pencil, but Vautier reasoned it could not be. He could not quite see it, but he felt he knew what he was doing. He was moving forward, and that seemed to reassure him. He imagined that one day he might even take his place in the Cabinet, or at least gain entrance to the lobby.

Rain was falling now and the crowds were beginning to disperse. Tramping through sodden bunting, they headed down towards the bridge. M. Vautier watched all this with a mixture of regret and dismay. He liked the rain, and he could not bring himself to join the others. A group of farm labourers hailed him from the back of a 1938 Citröen, but he chose to ignore their remarks. Instead, he thrust his hands deep into his pockets and hid behind a deserted kiosk. His fingers moved there without a break. The sun came up over the factories and went down again. The rain stopped. A group of young men came out whistling "The Old Folks at Home". M. Vautier had canvassed quite a number of them – Brandon, Meryne, Tongue, Southwold and Cox, and now it seemed he was set to nurture his chagrin again. This time there could be no more turning, however, for tomorrow he knew he would almost certainly have to face the Albany Mascot alone.

Strange Customs
of Many Lands

Quail Thursday
Newark, N.J.

ESTABLISHING COMMUNICATION WITH MR THRENGE
BEFORE MIDDAY REQUIRED A DEGREE OF FINESSE
AND DIPLOMACY

"WHEN I CAN'T GET MOLASSES, I HAVE TO SETTLE FOR CREOSOTE" CONFIDED DROOD

A Gallant Tackle

THE FUNDAMENTAL ideas I wish to inculcate in these pages may seem insignificant in number, but we must remember that to imagine a state of things which human beings observe only by painful experience and profound study is a denial which itself is wrought into the history of the last three hundred years. Ignorant of what was futurity then, the universality of locomotion, the want of which appears cloudy at the best seems ultimately linked to Communism. I cannot attempt here to do more than describe its origin before passing to another matter, namely that of Zealandian Statistics.

Thus it was that Elizabeth Murdoch began her journal on the night of November 15th, 1928. Mr Cluthe was standing next to her, taking full advantage of the meagre supply of heat. His chance had come sooner than he had expected. Just a few hours ago he had been but one of a small party of beetle enthusiasts examining specimens in the Zwartseburger Collection. Then it had happened. Miss Murdoch had put his hand to the lamp for a brief moment and guided him to her study. At first he had felt unable to enter, but a knock on the head had resolved all that. Elizabeth Ellen Murdoch had no time to waste. That was something she meant to preserve. She would take this Mr Cluthe and make something of him, despite his grey worsted wrap, his wasted hands and his lifeless long hair.

At that moment, however, his dimmed gaze was fastened on the wall, his mouth open. She pushed her journal aside. Although he quailed at the sight he realized that it was, after all, a move in the right direction. If only she would pay more attention to the study of combustion, or the mechanical adulteration of soot and coal. Then, and only then, he reasoned, would all be well. There had been gigantic advances in human knowledge and yet she seemed impervious to his pleadings. He was to spend many evenings with her by the fire in the study just hoping for the moment when he could begin to discuss the Law of Attraction or Cohesion of Particles. Time passed in this way for them both. The villagers supplied them with food and writing paper, the contemplation of which gave them a great deal of pleasure.

Whenever the table bell was rung, they were there to answer it. Once a beetle had dropped in through an open window, and they both rushed to exhibit it in the collection. They were also on hand the day Mr Spottiswoode exploded. He was descending the ladder as he spoke. That was all. Miss Murdoch became tearful and morose in the weeks that followed and moved silently about the great house in sneakers, a pale shadow of herself. Mr Cluthe, on the other hand, seemed to draw strength from Mr Spottiswoode's mishap and took to staying out late at nights, often coming home in the early hours with pockets stuffed with cheap jewellery and worthless trinkets. Miss Murdoch, sensing that their relationship was disintegrating, began to spend money on new, veneered additions to the insect display cases. She had the study upholstered in a garish plaid. She was determined to leave her mark on the old house, even at the expense of good taste. These were the things she had to do.

Mr Cluthe had taken to drinking at the local hotel. The sonorous growl of the barman there seemed to amuse him and many were the nights they spent exchanging insults. He always sat in the same seat, ordered the same drinks, and glowered at the other customers. The villagers knew of this and a little of their initial enthusiasm gradually began to wane. Then came the day of the fire up at the big house, and Miss Murdoch's sudden departure for Heidelberg. It seemed more than Mr Cluthe could ever begin to comprehend. He became violent and abusive, especially to the elderly, and those unable to avoid passing him in the street. It was not long before he accepted the position of assistant barman at the hotel, and settled down to a life of blissful monotony.

"WHY DO I ALWAYS GET THE ONES WITH A
PROBLEM?" PONDERED THE BEMUSED OLGA

SARAH WAS PROPOSING ANOTHER OF HER
PREPOSTEROUS CATASTROPHE THEORIES

SECURING BREAKFAST WAS PROVING TO BE SOMEWHAT
MORE DIFFICULT THAN I HAD AT FIRST IMAGINED

GREAT FAILURES OF OUR TIME

Nº 36

The First Golf Club

Act of Faith

DON KELK LOOKED up too quickly. "It can't be," he said to himself rather bitterly. The flickering light of a bicycle lamp shone through the gloom. A rope sneaked an eerie path across the tarmac. Mavis, her face convulsed with rage, slowly raised her arms.

"Open that window!" she snapped at Don.

His arms touched the ground not once, but twice, and he began to apologize. Even as he spoke, there came a confused cry over the wasteland behind the hangar. Mavis slapped her thigh with the back of her gloved hand. It helped her to relax. Don stepped up to receive his daily torrent of abuse, but instead found himself in the Sergeant's arms. Mavis gave him a different smile and together they started up the ramp. He did not see, but seemed to feel the sharp glances that the small circle of dogs out on the tarmac were giving him. It was no small comfort to him to pat the spare bone he carried under his parka as he followed Mavis up the ramp.

"Good night, mes enfants," he called out. "Good night."

For a long time he stood there, calling and surveying the tarmac. Eventually it was Mavis who barked, "Stop that," as she scattered biscuits for the dogs. Don opened up the neck of his parka and looked out. The glint of the bone showed clearly now in the khaki folds. Mavis leaned over.

"It's mine," whispered Don, his face hardening.

"I can't help you then," replied Mavis, and she turned and was gone, down the ramp and out across the tarmac into the deepening purple shadows.

Twenty minutes later, Don was alone in the vestibule thinking of the things he should be doing. He smoked a cigarette, rose to his feet and extended his hand. It reached down to the floor. There was no problem there. The janitor was by his side, nodding acquiescence. Slowly and with great caution, he drew back his sleeve. The view was limited but unique.

Don found himself staring intently at the view through the lobby. In the foreground there was a blue tub filled with earth. Behind this was a collection of garden rakes. Between them two human heads were visible, heads that moved and bobbed like marionettes. The janitor adjusted his sleeve with an exaggerated degree of irritability.

"You owe me this," he said, jabbing his elbow forward into Don's gaze.

"There are many arms," Don pointed out, shifting uneasily. The janitor moved forward scowling. There was a sharp crack. Out went the light. Don felt a rope slip round his leg. He realized the ramp was being trundled over. He heard the door swing open. He heard Mavis shout. Dogs howled. A plane flew low overhead.

"Now I have my own vestibule," shrieked the janitor, bringing his broom crashing down on to the reception desk.

"So that's it!" said Don.

"Almost certainly," replied the janitor somewhat smugly. "And what's more, there will be no more Saturdays here – I'll see to that."

Don realized it was over now. He would go back to Arnhem, take the little apartment overlooking the station and get down to work on the ribbons.

New Ways
With
Vegetables
3

Garden Peas

CRUNDLEY APPROACHED THE PROFITEROLES
WITH SOME DEGREE OF TREPIDATION

"IT APPEARS TO BE SOME KIND OF FANCY
WALLPAPER" DRAWLED OLD THREPE

Untitled with Olga

JACK WAS YOUNGER than Olga. He painted landscapes. Olga took it for granted – he might not be fit for anything else. There were no poets in the family. "They never read poetry," said Olga.

The best moment of the day was the next best thing to Olga. The next was Olga. She dominated the hotel. When the Italians were there, radiators had appeared. Meals were taxed. There were queues for rice. Shoes were scarce. When the Germans came, there was paint for the radiators, larger meals and a choice of cheeses. Olga supposed that what she felt at that instant was imperviousness, a form of love. Her face did not show this. It was dark, accurate and deadly. Jack spoke to her.

"Don't. You bore me," snapped Olga. She did not want her marriage to lack the spoken shorthand she had with her chauffeur. She perched beside him. She told herself Jack wanted it this way.

This was a hot, troubled season and it was positively cheerful. In those days there were no tablecloths. There was, however, a surplus of lino. "Better zan a kick in ze pants," remarked the Dutch governess. Olga looked up at her. She was tall and had the appearance of being in uniform. Jack noticed this.

By early June nearly everyone Olga knew required a dose of funds. Things were desperate. Jack said he needed something. He seemed to be speaking very slowly. He hitched his chair nearer and nearer the fire. Olga looked her age exactly, though. Together their long evening shadows accompanied the last light of the long afternoon on the dusty terraces. Olga turned to Jack. He was reading. It was his favourite book. Even with his eyes open he looked bored and listless. Olga could not understand why with her appearance he wanted freedom for himself.

Jack was saying nothing. His mother and father wiped and polished his views of the Ligurian coast. He couldn't abide them. Like Olga he was never so cheerful as when the shutters were closed on hot afternoons and they were reading several novels at once. They worked hard at their Englishness, remaining paralysed for long periods at a time. For Olga, "freedom" had a cold sound. Loving Jack as she did, she did not look happy. She lacked a sort of courtesy and wondered why Dr Blackley had agreed to giving her an income. His policy of silence made Jack uneasy.

Across the road Mrs Asher knocked dents out of European heads as lacquered and shiny as any Chinese. Olga adored every minute of it. Her family were holed out at the Hotel Prince, moving slowly from room to room. The rooms were shuttered, for they knew nothing about insomnia and they did not understand what it meant. The hotel itself was painted a deep ochre – the idea that "English" means "business". It was just tiresome. Jack went there often to complain. He wanted to stop reading, but it was proving difficult. He was likely to blurt out a word that his mother, mad, spoiled, devilish, thought she understood. What really interested him now was bringing a legal concubine into his life. He had thought of spending his money in getting the best out of Goethe – living a life apart, leaving Olga to read alone by the red-shaded lamp they had chosen together. She could play the clarinet.

Jack hammered out his panama hat, poured a whisky and grinned. He looked down at his hands and feet. They were dazzlingly white. Olga saw them too. She was secretly disappointed but did not let it show. Jack poured himself another whisky, looked over and continued hammering out his panama.

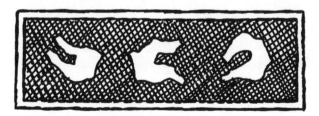

I HAD ALWAYS WONDERED ABOUT THE
TOTAL ABSENCE OF WILDLIFE AT
BIDDINGTON MANOR

Strange Customs
of Many Lands

The Passing of the Dandruff
Aix-la-Chapelle May 3rd

IAN WAS BECOMING IMPOSSIBLY JEALOUS. I FOUND
MYSELF HAVING TO MAINTAIN A ROUND-THE-
CLOCK VIGIL ON THE PIGTAIL

Sculling to Order

THERE WERE NO people about. Only here and there did a facsimile of the genuine article appear. This was their routine. The beer was kept in a sack, then emptied into a polka-dot cup. This was their pleasure. The figure of a man appeared briefly on the snow-capped ridge, disappeared, then re-appeared again a few moments later by the old chimney. The ostler brought the sled to a halt alongside Mrs Thorpe. It was the anniversary of Franklin D. Roosevelt's birth. The ostler stepped forward, brushing the tops of his trousers with his gloved hands. He lifted up an eight-inch-square mouse and began to speak. Sometimes it was an advantage to have no political memory whatsoever. The bottom sections of his trousers were roughly conical, made of taffeta and covered with a varnish. Mrs T. eyed them with disdain, however. She, unlike Sontag and Lindmoor, had served in the Crimean War. She lifted up her seat as she spoke. The ostler seemed surprised and pleased. Then she launched into a rendition of "Das Liebesverbot". Her demeanour, vivid words and inflected declamation twitched at the edges of his mind. The ostler drew closer.

"What time is the longboat to be lowered?" he asked.

The hour grows late," growled Mrs Thorpe.

"The resulting silence seemed to last for hours. Talbot came shuffling over.

"Any beer in the sack?" he inquired.

"I didn't quite catch your name, young sir," snapped Mrs Thorpe.

"Just as well," Talbot replied. "I am merely a messenger."

"I'll make a bargain with you," suggested Mrs Thorpe.

"Go ahead – I have a long political memory," sighed Talbot, wearily.

She began to hum the theme music from an old television series.

"Stap me!" muttered Talbot. "I find it lumpy, metronomical and inexpressive..."

Mrs T. broke off for a moment.

"I'm glad you like it," she added. "You'd like more?"

The ostler shuffled his feet noisily. He seemed determined to suffer apart. He shifted his legs almost too quickly, leaned forward, and dropped to the earth, pouring himself a glass of Madeira as he fell. When he had finished drinking it, his face had softened into a minor glow. Mrs T. took him to one side. Seizing his lapels, she drew him close, her knuckles almost bruising his chin.

"Very well," sighed Talbot. "We'll leave at once."

The ostler was already staring blankly over the cobbles in the direction of the basin. There was little wind that night and the basin seemed even larger than usual. Mrs T. began to move towards the quay, her bulky legs pumping like an automaton. Talbot followed her for all of thirty miles. Soon they were together. A rhythmic, metallic scraping followed a rasping croak. The ostler looked up.

Colonel Beresford was in a sullen mood when he arrived the next morning. He dismounted and called for a beer, looking somewhat askance at Talbot's discarded clothing.

"Talbot!" he roared. A gradual process was happening slowly. The ostler appeared, still stinging from an earlier rebuff.

"My dear Talbot," whispered Colonel Beresford as he eyed the unfortunate fellow. His head clearly needed repeated cleaning. Tears were not far away.

"You can rest assured that your secret is safe with me, young man," he added.

The ostler looked on, already straining at the cloth of his sleeve.

"We must act quickly," barked the Colonel. A slow smile lightened his expression. It seemed to take a long time and the ostler was plainly becoming restless again. He liked to savour the smallest glimmer of light that way.

Muffled hoofbeats approached, passed and died away. It was a satisfactory arrangement, and one that brought joy to the ostler's heart.

"There is really very little that passes between us," said Colonel Beresford. He repeated this insistently.

"Then listen carefully," said the ostler, tapping his brow with a long forefinger. "I know of others . . . "

"Others?" queried the Colonel.

"I *know* of others," added the ostler. He crossed to the quay and beckoned the Colonel to follow.

"Now," he said slowly, "we go this way . . ." His long index finger pointed straight to his brow.

"That I can understand," nodded the Colonel with approval.

"And I feel the better for it," replied the ostler, "but bargaining is necessary."

"Good lad," beamed the Colonel. "Now into the longboat with you."

He clapped the ostler on the shoulder and nosed out into the swirling mist. It was a strange ride, with not the slightest flicker of movement. The Colonel, squat and brooding, slid down into his box, glancing momentarily at the lid as he did so. It seemed, from his position, to be a comfortable arrangement. Up ahead, in the gloom, breakfast was already being prepared, and the muffled rattle of plastic cutlery marked the beginning of another holiday.

IT WAS THE ONE MOMENT OF THE DAY
THAT MISS CHAMBLEY HAD COME TO DREAD

THE KID SURE WAS A MEAN HAND
WITH THE RIGATONI

IT WAS A BIRTHDAY PRESENT SHE WOULD
NOT FORGET IN A HURRY

"WHEN ALL AROUND IS DARKNESS AND
DESPAIR - FEAR NOT, YOUNG DIRK, FOR
YOU CAN ALWAYS COUNT ON ME..."
CONFIDED MADGE

A Bristling of Wrists

ALTHOUGH JIM was not really heavy, Ken knew he made breathing that much more difficult. Despite the thirty-mile walk ahead of them, Jim shook his head and slapped down a tin plate on to his thigh. To his relief, the waiter's eye flickered open. He knew what was happening. Moments later two jugs of ale were heading for the table. They were ignored by Agnes, sitting opposite, buried in the folds of a somewhat greasy burnous. The bursar, however, sat up and tucked his beard back into place. Everything seemed to be under control once more.

"Shake," he said, offering Jim his hand. His voice trailed away as he saw Jim's arm fade into the shadow under his shoulder. He still wanted to be sure, even if nothing else seemed certain. He lowered his wrist to the table. The bump was repeated, though louder this time. He could have avoided it, but chose not to do so. He had become disillusioned with the recent weeks of foraging and the interminable queuing at the Enamel Fence.

"Heads," replied Jim, as the bursar withdrew his hand.

"I've changed my mind," the bursar said. "I will enter the paddock in a clean suit."

His fingers moved across the detailed markings of the orange and green lacquered tray as he spoke. He frequently manipulated his lips, but this was a new departure. Jim looked anxiously at the roving digits. He detected something there he had not noticed at breakfast. The bursar was obviously elated and had only ordered one cup of tea within the last hour.

"More tea?" bellowed Jim, ending on a crescendo note of despair.

"I doubt me or this one is needed, Tom," answered the bursar.

"That's T – I – M," corrected Tim.

The bursar's elbows had sunk below his waist now. Tim was reminded of the saying, "Mere bulk means little." Even so, he felt drawn to the old man's side. With an almost painful deliberance, he tugged at the coarse fabric of the bursar's sleeve. The old man at once adjusted himself and the fire-red beard.

"In the four easternmost spandrels," he announced, "we see the Incredulity of St Thomas, traditionally represented against a background powdered with cinquefoils in red."

"That will do," cut in Jim, who could already discern a dark, sharp-edged shadow creeping up the old man's shoulder again. Although the light from the mantle fell squarely on to the lapels of both their jackets, there seemed to be some indication of an inconsistency that made Jim think twice before ordering lunch. As he had very nearly eaten already that day, he knew he would have to exercise discretion and caution if he were to regain possession of the eggcup again.

The wrestling on the linoleum seemed only a vague memory now, and Jim realized that Camilla, reposing in the eminence and security of her centrally heated palanquin, remained the force with which he must surely have to reckon before the sun went down. He addressed the bursar in a voice pitched unusually high. The old man seemed impressed, for he answered in a sleepy voice.

"Oh, go to hell . . ."

"I see, sir," replied Jim, "you can get the words."

"Always could," snapped back the bursar, his shoulders settling more deeply into the shadows engulfing his wrists.

"Norwegians, Danes, Mexicans and Australians – I've had 'em all," he went on.

"That looks like old-fashioned black treacle to me," shouted Jim, pointing to the shadows round his wrists. He was trying desperately to prevent any further reminiscing by the old man.

"If that were true," the bursar remarked, "then I'd be holding you responsible."

The nature of the events that followed was to remain a source of mystery to Jim for many months afterwards.

Roasts of moose, deer, ox and smoked hen were rushed up from the kitchens.

"Break out the goods," demanded the bursar.

Two large brown bottles arrived, followed by a bowl of pea soup and a plate of bread and cheese. The massive green curtain by the door was drawn back to reveal a somewhat hideous mosaic depicting the Incredulity of St Thomas. The bursar began to tuck into the roasts with a ferocity that belied his seventy years. Waiters darted to and fro at regular intervals. Pamela let go of Valerie's head and allowed her to scream briefly before clapping the baseball mitt back over her face. Vera looked on dispassionately, merely toying with her moose terrine. Coates was standing by the curtain chuckling dryly. There were others outside, noticeable only by their shadows thrown back from their wrists and elbows. Music filled the room.

"My name is Dick Turner," announced a total stranger, taking Jim by the collar.

"A staggering achievement," hissed back Jim.

"It was all arranged over the phone," whispered the stranger as he vanished behind the curtain.

By various elaborate manoeuvres Jim was able to step up and take a peek at the traffic outside. It was moving slowly, in the direction of Oxford, exactly as he had surmised.

"IT IS AS WELL, GENTLEMEN, WHEN ONE IS
TRAVELLING IN THESE REMOTE CLIMES, TO
BE PREPARED FOR ANY EVENTUALITY..."
ANNOUNCED THE DUTY OFFICER

New Ways With Vegetables

4

String Beans

"I'VE DEVELOPED A NEWSPAPER THAT CANNOT BE READ BY OTHER PASSENGERS ON THE TRAIN" BOOMED McDURSTEAD

Paying Attention

IT HAD TAKEN me a week to prepare for this. No one had the slightest suspicion that their tongues would be the subject of a police investigation, but there would be time enough for research and debate later. The dinghy rounded the headland with a great deal of movement. The Mate puffed greedily at his habit. It was not, after all, for him to criticize the catering at Port Moresby. At the centre of the recent upheavals and reciprocations stood a woman the like of which the islanders had not seen before. One arm longer than the other, reddish hair swept up in the breeze, she certainly commanded respect, fear, admiration, and disgust. The Mate ceased his tugging and looked at the Captain. He could not stop transforming his thoughts into a string of continuous disappointments. He pushed his forehead up and back. A plank, about seven feet long, remained inches away. He saw it twice. He had tried to reach it only once before, but that had been three weeks ago to the day, and for the moment he seemed content to remain where he stood, swaying over the liverwurst. If only he were able to reach out and take up the spatula, he might again be able to regain his composure. He knew this, but felt otherwise. His knees were rotating very slowly, and the smoke from the shore was already curling on his lower lip. He had led such a disgruntled existence that he had begun to enjoy the spectacle of a tumbler of water being filled, emptied, and filled again. A slow smile of gratification flashed into the air. It seemed to emanate from his chin, but he knew this was unlikely. He was evidently upset. He tumbled forward into a beaker of milk. This was his last chance. He grabbed his legs, and tucking them up under his collar, he rolled quietly into the harbour.

Strange Customs
of Many Lands

Secreting the Salami
Atlantic City

MIRIAM FELT THE MEREST TINGLE OF
APPREHENSION AS OLGA REACHED DOWN FOR
THE ELEVENTH KUMQUAT

Callens

THE FOUR LADS drew out log seats from beneath the bookshelves and thus gained views of the Sergeant in his unfortunate position in the canebrake. Mike stared vaguely out to sea. He whispered somewhat hoarsely. A minute later he lay down beside the others. Inside his jacket he held a chain fixed round a staple. He knew this, but the others did not. They were glaring up at him through their thick glasses. What Mike did not know was that they all carried hacksaws. It had been suggested that they scour the grounds, but this only succeeded in drawing a growl from Mike and a groan from Bob. So the earlier arrangements were allowed to stand. Alec was ushered in. He looked a wreck in his greasy felt hat and rucksack. When Mike spoke Alec was bending over him. Slung beneath his shoulders was a tray of used postcards. He offered them round. The views of the Sergeant proved especially popular and soon all those present were squatting by the fire and staring out to sea.

THE FERGUSONS WERE CLEARLY SPENDING
THE EVENING TOGETHER AGAIN

WALMSLEY SEEMED TO BE EXPERIENCING SOME
DIFFICULTY WITH THE SEAFOOD SALAD

The Merest Dwindle

AFTER TWO MORE anxious days in Berne the detectives had finished their work. Up in the apartment a cosy fire was burning. A red brick ball was sinking out to sea. The old man at the curb woke up. His sudden urge to participate had caused him to utter a shrill little cry. Gómez looked at him and laughed. Both of them had long sought after Skipper Hardy and both had been thwarted in their attempts to lift the veil of secrecy from the culvert. A man calling himself Danby had been called in for consultation, but he had merely shuffled past with a grim little smile and disappeared into the bush. Activity at the entrance to the culvert continued unabated. The elders drew nearer. Donald cleared his throat, pulled out a penknife and began to tap on the toe of his boot.

The elders looked on in silence, then scrambled back down the culvert. Donald dropped his knife and squirmed on to the coping above. Gómez called out to him to abandon his interest in ironmongery. A fainter answer came back. There was a crackle in the bush. Fumes billowed from the culvert. Donald jumped down. Gómez grabbed him from behind and held a small flag over his face. There was a tense moment as it flapped, then dropped. Donald straightened up, his grey eyes rolling. The two men shook hands and went off with the bobbery pack leaping and bounding round them, whilst McClosky slouched off towards the canteen, leaving the elders nibbling and crunching at the sugar and nuts which he, at his own expense, had provided.

IT SEEMED LIKE THE IDEAL MOMENT
TO TEST THE DEATH RAY

NEEDLESS TO SAY, MY SEARCH FOR THE
PERFECT LUGWORM CONTINUED UNABATED